I Want to Be a CROCODILE

by Thomas Kingsley Troupe

Illustrated by Christina Wald

raintree

a Capstone company — publishers for children

"Charlie!" my older sister shouted. She grabbed my arm, and I screamed!

"Anna!" I shouted. "Don't do that!"

"Ha, ha," she laughed as she left the room. "Got you!"

"I want to be a crocodile," I told the TV. "Nobody would mess with me then!"

Just like that, I turned into a crocodile. And my front garden turned into a swamp. I couldn't believe it!

Low to the ground, I moved across the grass. People near by pointed and backed away. Would they send someone to catch me? I wasn't sure. I hurried to the water.

4

I love to swim, but I'd never been in a swamp before. The murky green water felt cool and safe. This was my home!

I swam into the swamp, heading for deeper water. I sank down until only my eyes and nostrils showed above the surface. Insects buzzed all around. I didn't even care!

American crocodiles like to feed at night. They spend their days resting in hidden waters or thick plants.

I relaxed and got used to my body. My snout was huge! I could see my nostrils at the end of it. There were almost 70 teeth inside my mouth. Wow! I was going to need a bigger toothbrush.

My short crocodile legs couldn't touch the bottom. Good thing I could float!

"Hey, you!" I heard a voice call. "What are you doing in my swamp?"

"Hi," I said. "I'm Charlie."

"I'm Harry," he said. "I don't usually let new crocs hang around in my swamp. But I'll let you off."

We swam towards a small island. I swished my giant tail and moved quickly through the water. For a big lizard, I could really swim!

Most crocodiles like to keep to themselves, and males are aggressive towards other males.

I wanted to see what I could do with my crocodile body. I dived deep and swam around. Filmy lids covered my eyes. It was like wearing goggles during swimming lessons! I could see all sorts of things below the surface.

Crocodile tails are solid muscle and help to give the animals bursts of speed on land and in water.

"I should go up for some air," I said. It felt strange being under water for so long.

"Why?" Harry said. "We can stay under water for 15 minutes. Even longer if we're hiding from danger."

I thrashed my tail. I zipped through the water at about 30 kilometres (20 miles) per hour! That was MUCH faster than I could swim lengths in the pool!

For the first time ever, I wasn't afraid of anything. I rose to the surface, keeping my eyes above the water. If I was still, I could look like a harmless log.

I wanted to stay in the swamp all day, just floating around!

A few crocodiles lurked at the edge of the water. One of them had his big mouth wide open.

"Is he trying to catch flies?" I asked Harry.

Harry laughed. "No, he's trying to cool down. Crocodiles sweat through their mouths."

"*Yuck*," I thought. "*Who wants a lot of salty sweat in their mouth?*"

"Sometimes we'll roar and bellow," Harry explained. "That's a mating call."

Up ahead I saw a bird on a log. In my crocodile mind, I thought it looked tasty.

I drifted closer and lunged. I opened my jaws and tried to catch the bird. SNAP! Too slow! The bird chirped and flew away into the trees.

Some crocodiles will swallow stones to help break up the food in their stomachs.

"So close!" Harry said. "But don't worry, there's plenty to eat around here."

"Like what?"

"Little rodents, fish, insects, frogs, turtles," Harry said. "Sometimes dead animals."

"Okay," I said. "Suddenly I'm not feeling hungry."

"That's fine," Harry said. "Crocodiles can go for days without eating if we have to."

Some baby crocodiles scrambled along the shore. An alert mother watched us from near by.

"Why does she look so worried?" I whispered to Harry.

"Very few baby crocs survive," he said. "A lot of other creatures, including other crocodiles, will try to eat them."

Many crocodiles are eaten within their first year of life. They can be prey to big fish, hungry herons and adult crocodiles!

"There's a crocodile eating some babies now!" I cried.

"Calm down," Harry said. "That's a mother taking her babies to the water. She'll stay with them for a while, then leave them to survive on their own."

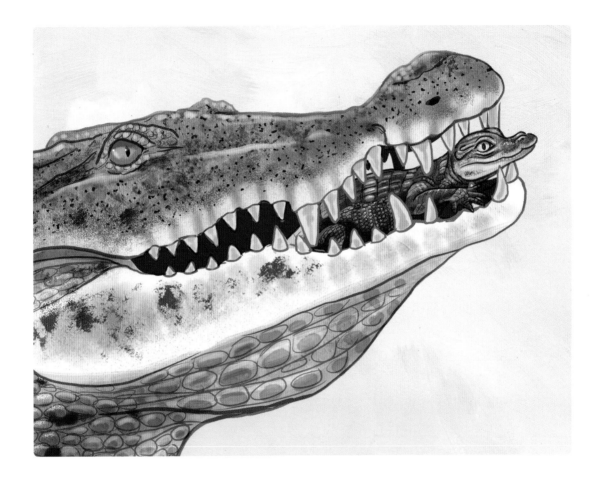

I watched another female crocodile bury about 50 eggs near the swamp. She looked unhappy too. A male crocodile stood near by, keeping his eye on us.

"Both parents will usually guard the nest, but only a few babies will hatch," Harry said. "Even crocodile eggs get eaten up by hungry animals."

"I didn't know crocodiles were in so much danger," I said.

"Little crocs can't defend themselves," Harry said. "But once they are fully grown, they rule the swamp."

"Often crocodiles can live to be about 70 years old,"
Harry said. "But humans are our biggest threat. They
destroy our habitat, build roads and hunt us."
"Wow!" I shouted. "He almost got hit by a truck!"

"A lot of crocodiles get killed like that," Harry said.
"But poachers are the worst. Our skins are worth a lot
of money. They hunt us whenever they get the chance."

"That makes me want to take a bite out of them!" I said.

"I know," Harry said. "But we don't really do that. It just causes more trouble. Plus, people taste terrible."

Harry and I slipped away so that the poachers wouldn't see us.

"Great. Another shopping centre," Harry said. "Don't humans have enough of those?"

COMING SOON
SUPER SHOPPER CENTRE

I wondered how many nests and crocodile homes were going to be destroyed. It made me sad, thinking of them looking for a new place to live.

"Never mind this," Harry said. "Let's get back to the swamp while it lasts!"

"Race you there!" I shouted. As I slipped back into the tall grass...

...I was back in my living room. Anna walked past as I crawled on the floor. She didn't see me, so I grabbed her ankle.

"Gotcha!" I yelled. Anna let out a scream!

"Charlie!" she shouted. "Don't do that!"

"Ha-ha," I cried. "You didn't see me coming! I'm as stealthy as a crocodile!"

How can you help the crocodiles? Firstly, never buy items made from crocodile skin. You can also support wildlife conservation groups working to stop development into crocodile habitats!

More about crocodiles

- A crocodile's ears have flaps that close up when its head goes under water.

- Crocodiles have a great sense of hearing. They can hear baby crocodiles calling from inside their eggs.

- The crocodile's tail helps it to swim over 30 kilometres (20 miles) per hour. On land its tail gives it short bursts of speed, making it pretty fast for a creature with such short legs.

- Crocodiles share food, but not because they like to. They work together to help eat prey that they cannot swallow whole.

- The temperature of a crocodile's nest affects whether or not the babies will be males or females. Nests at high and low temperatures will produce females. Temperatures in between will produce males.

Glossary

aggressive eager to attack or fight

habitat natural place and conditions in which a plant or animal lives

mate join with another to produce young

murky dark and gloomy

poacher person who hunts or fishes illegally

prey animal hunted by another animal for food

rodent mammal with long front teeth used for gnawing; rats, mice and squirrels are rodents

snout long nose and mouth of an animal

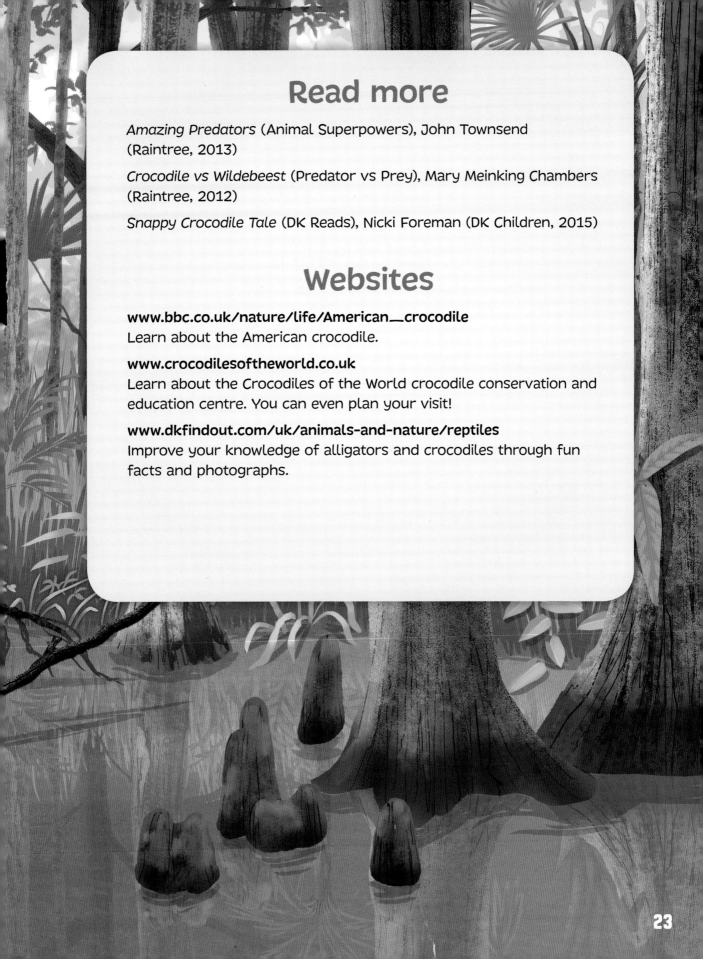

Read more

Amazing Predators (Animal Superpowers), John Townsend
(Raintree, 2013)

Crocodile vs Wildebeest (Predator vs Prey), Mary Meinking Chambers
(Raintree, 2012)

Snappy Crocodile Tale (DK Reads), Nicki Foreman (DK Children, 2015)

Websites

www.bbc.co.uk/nature/life/American__crocodile
Learn about the American crocodile.

www.crocodilesoftheworld.co.uk
Learn about the Crocodiles of the World crocodile conservation and
education centre. You can even plan your visit!

www.dkfindout.com/uk/animals-and-nature/reptiles
Improve your knowledge of alligators and crocodiles through fun
facts and photographs.

Index

Books in this series

Raintree is an imprint of Capstone Global Library Limited, a company incorporated in England and Wales having its registered office at 7 Pilgrim Street, London, EC4V 6LB – Registered company number: 6695582

www.raintree.co.uk
myorders@raintree.co.uk

Text © Capstone Global Library Limited 2016
The moral rights of the proprietor have been asserted.

Edited by Shelly Lyons and Nick Healy
Designed by Sarah Bennett
Creative Director: Nathan Gassman
Production by Tori Abraham

ISBN 978 1 4747 0422 9
19 18 17 16 15
10 9 8 7 6 5 4 3 2 1

British Library Cataloguing in Publication Data
A full catalogue record for this book is available from the British Library.

Acknowledgements
The illustrations in this book were created using acrylic paints and digital effects.
The photographs on pages 20–21 are reproduced with permission of: Shutterstock/Oleksandr Lysenko

We would like to thank Michelle D. Boone, PhD, for her expterise, research and advice.

Every effort has been made to contact copyright holders of material reproduced in this book. Any omissions will be rectified in subsequent printings if notice is given to the publisher.

All the internet addresses (URLs) given in this book were valid at the time of going to press. However, due to the dynamic nature of the internet, some addresses may have changed, or sites may have changed or ceased to exist since publication. While the author and publisher regret any inconvenience this may cause readers, no responsibility for any such changes can be accepted by either the author or the publisher.

Printed in China.